Best Loved Stories

WHAT KATY DID

by Susan Coolidge

abridged edition

The Little Carrs

Katy's name was Katy Carr. She lived in the town of Burnet, which was not a big town, but was growing fast.

There were six Carr children — Katy, the oldest, was twelve; pretty little Phil, the youngest, was four, and the rest fitted in between. Dr Carr, their papa, was a kind, busy man, who was away from home all day and sometimes all night too, taking care of sick people. The children's mama had died when Phil was a baby, and in her place there was Aunt Izzie, papa's sister, who was a sharp-faced, neat and particular woman, who meant to be kind to the children, but who was very much puzzled by them. They were not gentle or tidy as she had been — Katy tore her dress every day and hated sewing, and she and her sisters cared not a button about being called "good".

Clover was a fair, sweet girl, with blue eyes that always looked ready to hold tears, although she was really the jolliest little thing in the world, sunny and sweet-tempered, modest about herself, and extremely droll and funny in a quiet way.

Elsie was a thin, brown child of eight with beautiful dark eyes and crisp, short curls covering her small head. Poor Elsie seemed to be the odd one out of the children, longing to be with Katy, Clover and Cecy Hall, but always being told by them to "run away and play with the children".

Dorry was six years old — a pale, pudgy boy, with rather a solemn face and smears of molasses on the sleeve of his jacket. Joanna, whom the children called "John" or "Johnnie", was a square, splendid child, a year younger than Dorry, with big brave eyes and a wide rosy mouth which always looked ready to laugh.

Cecy Hall was a great friend of Katy and Clover, and lived next door. She was a neat, pink and white girl, whose light shining hair never got tangled, and whose slim hands never looked dirty. How different from Katy! Katy's hair was always untidy; her frocks were always tearing themselves, and she was as heedless and careless as a child of six. Katy was the *longest* girl that was ever seen, up above papa's ear and half a head taller than Aunt Izzie. When she stopped to think about her height, she became very awkward, as if all her joints were sticking out at once at right angles. Luckily, Katy's head was so full of other things that this happened rarely. She had fits of responsibility about the younger children, longing to set them a good example, but generally she forgot to do so.

At the bottom of a field near the house was a marshy thicket that the children called "Paradise", and here they all went one day in spring. Aunt Izzie had packed them a delicious lunch, with cakes, sandwiches and molasses pies. Afterwards, they all pretended about the things they would do when they were grown up. Cecy wanted to be very good — to teach in Sunday School and visit the poor.

"And one day," she concluded triumphantly, "a poet will come along and see me, and he'll go home and write a poem about me!"

Clover wanted to be the most beautiful lady in the world, and have a pond full of lavender water in her backyard. She would wear gold dresses and silver dresses, and diamond rings. Elsie wanted just the same, but insisted that her pond would be bigger — and there would have been tears if Clover had not hastily asked Johnnie what she wanted to be. Johnnie was not forthcoming, laughing a great deal and squeezing Dorry's arm very tightly. Dorry's future was very much concerned with what he would eat — and then it was Katy's turn.

"Well, I'll be beautiful, of course, and good, and I'll have a large house and a splendiferous garden, and we needn't do anything we don't want to — like darning stockings. But now I'll tell you what I want to *do*."

"Isn't it the same thing?" asked Clover, but Katy shook her head.

"I mean to *do* something grand. I don't know what yet. Perhaps I'll rescue people from shipwrecks, or nurse in a hospital, or lead a crusade. Or maybe I'll paint, or sing, or make figures in marble."

It seemed only a moment had passed before the evening came, and they had to leave Paradise. But it was very comforting to know that it would always be there.

Katy, Clover and Cecy went to Mrs Knight's

school, which was large and popular, and which stood next to Miss Miller's school, equally large and popular. A constant feud raged between the two schools as to their respective merits, and this took the form of making faces over the fence between the two yards.

One morning, Katy was late for school and was given a black mark, which made her irritable for the rest of the day. At break, she made her way to the woodshed roof, which overlooked the Miller yard. it was empty, as Miss Miller's clock was slow. Suddenly a strong gust of wind caught Katy's sun bonnet and whisked it away to lie, flapping, in Miss Miller's yard.

Katy was horrified! Their enemies would use it as a trophy of war — she must rescue it. Katy set her teeth and vaulted into the Millerites' yard, just as their break bell rang and the enemy poured outside.

There are moments when it is a fine thing to be tall. Quickly Katy grabbed her bonnet and leapt back up the fence, kicking out wildly at one Millerite who had seized her foot with cries of fury.

The Knights were beside themselves with pride and triumph, kissing and hugging Katy until, what with the excitement of her adventure and everything else, she became very reckless.

At lunchtime, her unlucky star put it into Katy's head to invent a new game, the Game of Rivers. Katy herself was Father Ocean, and the other girls each took the name of a river and rushed roaring about the classroom, until Father Ocean called them for a meeting of the waters, when they rushed towards him. The noise was horrifying, the mess still more so — as Mrs Knight found on her return from lunch.

The afternoon proceeded in stony silence, and after the bell rang, the rivers and Father Ocean were told to stay behind. Mrs Knight began to speak to them, and it was not long before they were all crying — Katy especially. All the way home she sobbed, while Clover trotted alongside her, begging her to stop crying and trying to mend her torn dress.

Later that evening, when the little ones had gone to bed, Katy sat on papa's knee and told him all about the day. She was so ashamed by the whole thing that she promised him that she would never get into any more scrapes.

Fun and Games

But the very next Monday saw Katy getting into another scrape.

Dr Carr was attending patients, and Aunt Izzie went out with Cecy's mother Mrs Hall to an evening lecture. Cecy came over, and after supper, they all began talking about Kikeri.

Kikeri was a game they had invented themselves — a mixture of Blind Man's Buff and Tag, but instead of anyone being blindfolded it was played in the dark. Whoever was caught had to take the place of the catcher. So many scratches and bruises came of it, and so many things got broken, that Aunt Izzie

had banned the game a year ago — but Dr Carr had not, and Aunt Izzie might now and then be defied, whereas he might not.

They all began to play, except Phil, who was asleep, and it was certainly splendid fun. Dorry got a hard knock and cried, and Katy's dress got caught and was terribly torn — but the fun and frolic seemed to grow greater the longer they played. Suddenly they heard the slam of a carriage door — Aunt Izzie had returned from her lecture!

Oh, the dismay and confusion! Cecy slipped downstairs and home like an eel, while upstairs in the Carr nursery, panic ruled. Katy scuttled off to her own room and bed with all possible speed, but the others found it much slower — there were so many of them in the dark. Dorry and John popped under the clothes half undressed, Elsie vanished, and Clover, too late to get into bed in any state, fell on her knees by a chair and began to say her prayers very hard indeed.

Aunt Izzie scolded her sharply, and found Dorry and John pretending to be asleep as hard as they could, still wearing their school boots. Elsie was discovered in her bed. She was still fully-dressed, but so sound asleep that none of Aunt Izzie's shakings and callings could rouse her, and she was the only one to escape the scolding that night.

Katy was lying in bed feeling guilty and ashamed for having drawn the others into a scrape. Aunt Izzie's severe words were almost a relief to her, and she cried herself to sleep.

The next day she cried even more, for Dr Carr spoke to her more seriously than ever before, about how she must take her mama's place with the younger children. Then he called all the children together and solemnly forbade them ever to play Kikeri again. And they have not done so to this day.

Imagine a low, dark loft without any windows, and with only a very little light coming in through the square hole in the floor where was the rough ladder. There was a strong smell of corn cobs, a great deal of dust and spider-webs, and some wet spots, for the roof always leaked in rainy weather. This was the place that the Carrs and Cecy preferred to any other on rainy Saturdays.

"Now," said Katy as they all got settled, "the Fete can commence."

Then the children read each other stories and poems they had written and afterwards the Feast was held, which consisted of cookies and a bottle full of weak vinegar-and-water, which every child christened differently. Clover called hers "Raspberry Shrub", Dorry's was "Ginger Pop", and Cecy's "Hydomel", which she explained was something nice and romantic made of beeswax. It may not sound like very much, but none of the children could eat their tea later on, though all agreed that the afternoon had been "splendiferous!"

Intimate Friends

"Aunt Izzie, may I ask Imogen Clark to spend the day here on Saturday?" cried Katy, bursting in one afternoon. "She's perfectly beautiful! She's got the littlest waist of any girl in school, and she's so sweet and so self-denying and unselfish! Do let me ask her!"

Aunt Izzie was reluctant, but Katy's pleading face moved her to agree. Poor Katy! Her tendency to fall violently in love with new people was always getting her into scrapes, and her 'intimate friends' had been one of the household jokes since she could walk and talk.

Imogen's real name was Elizabeth. She was naturally a bright girl, but she had read so many novels that her brain was completely turned. On the Saturday everyone worked very hard to make themselves and the house look spick and span — Katy and Clover built a beautiful bower of asparagus boughs under the trees.

When Imogen arrived, she was dressed in frilly clothes totally unsuitable for the play that the Carrs enjoyed, and her manner was very different from the one which had so enchanted Katy. She was fluttery and affected — she did not want to do any of the things the others wanted to do. She did not like the bower, she would not venture up the ladder into the loft, and instead preferred to sit with Katy and Clover in the best parlour, telling them romantic tales about her abduction by brigands and how the chief brigand had freed her because of her beauty.

The visit was evidently not a success. Papa was very civil to Imogen at dinner, but Katy saw a comical twinkle in his eyes as he looked at her that she did not like; Papa saw everything, and Katy began to feel low-spirited.

"Aren't you glad she's gone?" whispered Clover later, as they stood at the gate together, watching Imogen walk mincingly down the street.

"Oh, Clover! How can you?" said Katy. But she gave Clover a great hug, and I think in her heart she *was* glad.

Cousin Helen's Visit

School closed for the summer in July, and on arriving home Katy and Clover found the house in uproar.

"What *can* be going to happen? Aunt Izzie, who's coming? Why *are* you moving the things out of the Blue-room?"

Aunt Izzie looked very hot and flurried. "Your Cousin Helen is coming to visit us," she said curtly, and disappeared into the room.

This was news indeed! Cousin Helen coming! None of them had ever seen her; she rarely went away from home, and lay on a sofa all the time because she was ill and crippled. Katy imagined that she would be terribly patient and noble, and that they would have to creep around in stockinged feet all the time. But the real Cousin Helen was very dif ferent. She had a gay, pleasant, merry manner, and wore pretty clothes, and she hugged and kissed them as if she had wanted to do so all her life.

The Blue-room was transformed when Katy went in to see Cousin Helen the next morning. Pretty things had been scattered about it, and Katy admired in particular a graceful white vase which Cousin Helen took everywhere with her, to make her feel at home.

Very soon, all the children had come to see Cousin Helen, and Aunt Izzie, dropping in on them, was quickly drawn into their games. It was unheard of! Aunt Izzie sat on the floor with her hair half coming down and with three long paper spills stuck into it, playing in the jolliest manner, until Doctor Carr was quite ready to believe that Cousin Helen was a witch who had cast a spell over them all.

"It must be *awful* to be ill, though," thought Katy to herself. "Why, if I had to stay in bed a whole week, I should *die!*"

For the four days of Cousin Helen's visit, the children were always with her, but the four days were still over far too soon. Cousin Helen gave them all presents — to Katy she gave a vase exactly the same as her own that Katy had admired so much. When she had gone and Katy had wiped her eyes, she made a resolution that she too would try to be as good and kind as Cousin Helen.

Tomorrow

Katy's last sleepy thought was the intention to be an angel from that time on — but when she opened her eyes she was all out of sorts and as fractious as a bear!

You know how, if we begin the day in a cross mood, all sorts of accidents seem to happen. The first thing Katy did was to break the precious vase that Cousin Helen had given her. Katy cried as hard as if she had been little Phil, and then ate her breakfast in sulky silence.

Aunt Izzie forbade the younger children to use the new swing that had just been put up in the woodshed, but she did not say why, which was unwise. The truth was that one of the staples which fastened the swing to the roof was cracked and unsafe, but Aunt Izzie believed that children should do as they were told without explanation.

After breakfast Katy's bad temper led her into an argument with Elsie, during which Katy gave her little sister a vindictive push which sent Elsie sprawling down half a dozen stairs to the bottom. Katy was ashamed of herself, but too cross to admit to it and, angrily, she went outside.

The new swing immediately caught her eye. Ignoring what Aunt Izzie had said about not using it, she seated herself on it and began to swing, higher and higher, until she felt as if she was flying.

Suddenly there was a sharp cracking noise. The

swing gave a violent twist, spun half round and tossed Katy into the air. She clutched at the rope, but found herself falling down — down — down. All grew dark and she knew no more.

When Katy opened her eyes, she was lying on the sofa in the dining room. Clover and Aunt Izzie were with her, both looking pale and frightened. Katy tried to get up to go and lie on her bed, but found that she couldn't stand up.

Doctor Carr had gone to visit a patient in the country, so Doctor Alsop was called to come and examine Katy. He told them that Katy had certainly

done some damage to her back, and that she would have to stay in bed for some days.

Katy cried weakly as she lay in bed that afternoon — it was hot, flies buzzed around, and her head and back ached violently. Elsie came in after a while, closed the blinds and fanned her sister with a palm-leaf fan — she had brought Katy some presents from herself and Johnnie, a pewter tea-set, a doll, two pencils and other things. At the sight of all this Katy began to cry again, remembering how unkind she had been to Elsie, and the two hugged one another tightly.

The next day Doctor Carr returned to find a fever-ish Katy, who demanded to know if she would have to lie there for a week.

"My darling, I'm afraid you must," said Doctor Carr, who looked worried and very grave.

Dismal Days

There came a time when Katy didn't ask if she could get up. She had dreadful pains in her back, days and nights got tangled up together, doctors came and examined her and talked in hushed whispers, and it seemed that her only relief came with sleep. When at last she recovered from the fever four weeks later, her legs were heavy and lifeless, and she could not walk or even stand alone.

"I am afraid, my darling," Doctor Carr said to her one day, "that you must make up your mind to stay in bed a long time. I can't tell exactly how long. The doctors think that your injury is one which you will outgrow by and by. But it may take a good while to do it. You might have to lie here for months. It is hard," — for Katy began to sob wildly — "but you have hope. Think of Cousin Helen, bearing all these years without hope."

The six longest weeks of Katy's life were those which followed this conversation with Papa. She was miserable and wretched and had long fits of hopeless crying.

Luckily this ended with a further visit from Cousin Helen. The blinds were opened in Katy's room so that the sun could get in, and Cousin Helen encouraged Katy to make a pretty place out of her sickroom, so that the children would want to visit her. There seemed to be so many interesting and useful things she could do while lying down, and many lessons she would have to learn — patience, cheerfulness, making the best of things, hopefulness and neatness, as well as continuing her studies. When Cousin Helen left, Katy felt like crying, but managed bravely to hold back the tears.

"My first lesson in patience," she said to herself, and managed a faint, watery smile.

Cousin Helen's visit did great good to Katy, although of course she did not become perfect all at once. Winter had come and it was almost Christmas, and Katy was thinking about the presents she would give the others — a sash for Clover, a writing-desk for Elsie, a sled for Johnnie, books for Dorry, Cecy and Aunt Izzie, reins for Phil and some gloves for Papa.

The children hung their stockings up in Katy's room on Christmas Eve, and she and Aunt Izzie stuffed them full of gifts that night before Katy went to sleep.

Christmas brought her some surprises. The children had made a tiny Christmas tree for her, and there were presents for Katy all round it from them all, resting on a large and curious wheeled chair.

"That's Papa's present," said Clover. "See, it tips back so as to be just like a bed."

It was several weeks before she was able to lie on the chair, but when she was used to it it proved very comfortable, and Katy's joy at being able to watch the children playing outside from the window was unimaginable to anyone who has not, like Katy, had to lie on a bed for six months.

Very soon it was February and St Valentine's Day. Katy and Cecy put their heads together. There was a special tea in Katy's room in the late afternoon, with a cake dedicated to St Valentine — and then the Valentine cards arrived, one for each child, with rhymes inside written by Katy and Cecy, who had to pretend to be as surprised as the rest. There was a lot of laughter as each child read out their rhyme.

"Hasn't it been a jolly evening?" asked Johnnie.

"Yes," replied Dorry. "We never had such good times before Katy was ill, did we?"

Katy heard this with a mingled feeling of pleasure and pain. "I think the children love me a little more of late," she said to herself. "But oh! why couldn't I have been good to them when I was well and strong!"

A New Lesson to Learn

Spring was late that year, but the summer was a warm one, and Katy felt the heat very much. She could not follow the breezes about as other people could, and she wilted much as flowers do. But Katy's year of careful schooling in patience served her well, and rarely did she forget her resolutions and become fretful. There was nothing to do but wait for the cooler weather.

Katy seemed to revive in September. She asked Papa if she could take up her French lessons again, and he was delighted to agree that she could.

One day in November, Aunt Izzie had a headache. This was unusual in itself, but by noon she had a fever. That night, old Mary came to put Katy to bed, and Katy realised that she missed her aunt dreadfully.

Aunt Izzie's attack proved to be typhoid fever. John, Dorry and Phil were sent over to Mrs Hall's to stay, and Clover and Elsie crept about the house like mice. Then one morning, Katy woke up to find old Mary crying quietly. Aunt Izzie had died in the night.

Changes had to be made in the running of the household. Papa was in favour of hiring a housekeeper, but Katy pleaded with him not to do so. Instead she wished to try managing the household affairs herself. Papa was worried — she was very young to start doing so — but she pleaded and begged until he gave in and allowed her a month to prove that she was competent.

Actually, the house seemed to run itself, all the servants were so used to Aunt Izzie's punctual, regular ways. Of course Katy made mistakes, and sometimes had fits of over-anxiousness about the children, but these were only a beginner's natural mistakes, and Katy improved more and more as the weeks went by. Nothing more was said about "somebody else", and Katy, sitting upstairs in her big chair, held the threads of the house firmly in her hands.

Two years later, Katy was still in charge of the household. Her brothers and sisters loved to be with her, and do things for her, and her advice was asked for on every subject.

One day Mrs Worrett came to pay a call; she was an old friend of Aunt Izzie's, who lived in the country about six miles from Burnet. She sometimes came to the house for lunch on days when she came into town, but Katy had never entertained her before. Two years before, she would have jumped at the chance to tell Mrs Worrett she was too busy to see her, but now Katy was different. She arranged for some lunch to be brought up, and entertained the fat old lady politely and kindly, although the afternoon had surely never been so long.

At last Mrs Worrett prepared to leave. "Well," she said, "I wish your aunt could see you all as you are now. She'd be very pleased, I know that. It's not every girl would know how to take care of a fat old woman and make her feel at home, as you have made me, Katy."

About six weeks later, Katy called Clover and Elsie urgently to her room.

"Oh, what do you think?" she cried. "I stood up! Suddenly I had the feeling that if I tried I could, and almost before I thought, I *did* try, and there I was!"

Next day she did it again, and Papa was very excited when he told her that she was probably going to get well.

"But you *must* be careful," he told her, "or you'll be laid up again."

Katy's progress was slow. At first she practised standing, then walking step by step, with Clover and Elsie hovering anxiously nearby. Gradually she grew adventurous, and in the course of two or three weeks she was able to walk all over the first floor.

At last it was agreed that she would once more come downstairs, and the eighth of September, her mother's birthday, was fixed on as the date for this.

For the week beforehand, Clover and everyone else seemed very busy, and the day before the occasion Katy's door was kept shut while the hall was swept. Katy was puzzled; it was an odd time to sweep the hall. Sitting in her room, she could hear strange noises — feet running up and down stairs, doors opening and shutting, and muffled giggling.

The day came at last, and Papa supported Katy as she walked very slowly downstairs, all the children following them. Katy paused to admire some new things that had appeared since she was last downstairs, but Philly, who seemed to be very impatient about something, kept urging her on. So they moved on. Papa opened the parlour door. Katy took one step into the room, and stopped. There, lying on the sofa, was Cousin Helen. She held out her arms, and Katy, forgetting her disability, ran towards her.

A perfect hubbub of questions and exclamations followed. The idea of inviting Cousin Helen to see Katy come downstairs had been Clover's, and she had arranged everything. The sweeping of the hall had been deliberately arranged to stop Katy hearing the sounds of Cousin Helen's arrival the day before. Katy was overjoyed to see her cousin, but Cousin Helen was perhaps the happiest of the party. Besides seeing Katy almost well again, she could see how many changes for the better had taken place during the four years of Katy's illness, among the little cousins she loved so much.

"You have won the place," she said to Katy, "which I once told you an invalid should try to gain, of being to everybody 'The Heart of the House'."

Katy's eyes filled with sudden tears. "Oh, don't," she said, "I haven't been brave at all. I'm cross and ungrateful, and stupid and slow. Every day I see things which ought to be done, and I don't do them. I don't deserve your praise."

But although she said she didn't deserve it, I think Katy did!

Conic Section

It was wonderful to see how Katy gained and improved. It was like a miracle to the others, in the beginning, to watch her going about the house; but they got used to it surprisingly soon — one does to pleasant things. One person, however, never got used to it, and that was Katy herself. She could not run downstairs, or out into the garden; she could not open the kitchen door to give an order, without a sense of gladness beyond words. Her cheeks grew round and pink, her eyes bright. Cousin Helen and Papa watched this change with indescribable pleasure; and Mrs Worrett, who dropped in to lunch one day, fairly screamed with surprise at the sight of it.

"To think of it!" she cried. "Why, the last time I was here you looked as if you had taken root in that chair of yours for the rest of your days, and here you are stepping around as lively as can be! Well, well! wonders will never cease. It does my eyes good to see you, Katherine. I wish your poor aunt were here today; that I do. How pleased she'd be!"

Katy was touched at the genuine kindness of Mrs Worrett's voice, and took very willingly her offered kiss. Just before she went away, she said:

"How is it that I can never get any of you to come out to Conic Section? I'm sure I've asked you often enough. There's Elsie, now, and John; they're just the age to enjoy being in the country. Why don't you send them out for a week? Johnnie can feed chickens, and chase 'em too, if she likes," she added, as Johnnie dashed into view, pursuing one of Phil's bantams round the house.

Katy thanked her, but she didn't think the children would care to go. She gave Johnnie the message, and then the whole matter passed out of her mind. She was surprised, a few days later, by having it brought up again by Elsie. The family were in low spirits that morning because of Cousin Helen's having just gone away; and Elsie was lying on the sofa, fanning herself with a great palm-leaf fan.

"Oh, dear!" she sighed. "Do you suppose it's ever going to be cool again in this world? It does seem as if I couldn't bear it any longer. I keep thinking about the country, and wishing I was there feeling the wind blow. I wonder if Papa wouldn't let John and me go to Conic Section, and see Mrs Worrett. Do you think he would if you asked him?"

"But," said Katy, amazed, "Conic Section isn't exactly country, you know. It is just out of the city — only six miles from here. And Mrs Worrett's house is close to the road, Papa said. Do you think you'd like it, dear? It *can't* be very much cooler than this."

"Oh, yes! It can," rejoined Elsie, in a tone which was a little fretful. "It's quite near woods, Mrs Worrett told me so. Besides, it's *always* cooler on a farm. Won't you ask Papa if we may go, Katy?"

"Why, of course I will, if you wish it so much. Only—" Katy stopped and did not finish her sentence. A vision of fat Mrs Worrett had risen before her, and she could not help doubting if Elsie would find the farm as pleasant as she expected. But Elsie's eyes looked so wistful that Katy had no heart to argue or refuse.

Dr Carr looked doubtful when the plan was proposed to him.

"It's too hot," he said. "I don't believe the girls will like it."

"Oh, yes, we will, Papa; indeed we will," pleaded Elsie and John.

Dr Carr smiled at the imploring faces, but he looked a little quizzical. "Very well," he said, "you may go. Mr Worrett is coming into town tomorrow, on some bank business. I'll send word by him, and in the afternoon, when it is cooler, Alexander can drive you out."

"Goody! Goody!" cried John, jumping up and down, while Elsie put her arms round Papa's neck and gave him a hug.

"And on Thursday I'll send for you," he continued.

"But, Papa," expostulated Elsie, "that's only two

days. Mrs Worrett said a week."

"Yes, she said a week," chimed in John. "And she's got ever so many chickens, and I'm to feed 'em, and chase 'em about as much as I like. Only it's too hot to run much," she added, reflectively.

"You won't really send for us on Thursday, will you, Papa?" urged Elsie, anxiously. "I'd like to stay ever and ever so long; but Mrs Worrett said a week."

"I shall send on Thursday," repeated Dr Carr in a decided tone. Then, seeing that Elsie's lip was trembling and her eyes were full of tears, he continued: "If you want to stay longer, you may send back a note to say what day you would like to come home. Will that do?"

"Oh, yes," said Elsie, wiping her eyes. "That will do beautifully, Papa. Only it seems such a pity that Alexander should have to go twice when it's so hot; for we're perfectly sure to want to stay a week."

Papa only laughed as he kissed her.

The drive out was pleasant. Part of the way the road ran through woods. They were rather boggy woods; but the dense shade kept off the sun, and there was a spicy smell of evergreens and sweet fern. Elsie felt that the good time had fairly begun, and her spirits rose with every turn of the wheels.

By and by they left the woods, and came out again into the sunshine. The road was dusty, and so were the fields, and the ragged sheaves of cornstalks which dotted them here and there looked dusty too. Piles of dusty-red apples lay on the grass, under the orchard trees. Some cows going down a lane toward their milking-shed mooed in a dispirited and thirsty way, which made the children feel thirsty also.

"I want a drink of water very badly," said John. "Do you suppose it's much further? How long will it be before we get to Mrs Worrett's, Alexander?"

"'Most there, miss," replied Alexander.

Elsie put her head out of the carriage, and looked eagerly round. Where was the delightful farm? She saw a big, pumpkin-coloured house by the roadside, a little further on; but surely that couldn't be it! Yes; Alexander drew up at the gate, and jumped down to lift them out. It really was! The surprise quite took away her breath.

She looked about. There were the woods, to be sure, but half a mile away across the fields. Near the house there were no trees at all; only some lilac bushes at one side; there was no green grass either. A gravel path took up the whole of the narrow front yard; and, what with the blazing colour of the paint and the wide-awake look of the blindless windows, the house had somehow the air of standing on tiptoe and staring hard at something — the dust in the road, perhaps, for there seemed nothing else to stare at.

Elsie's heart sank. They turned the corner of the house, and there was Mrs Worrett waiting at the kitchen door to receive them. She looked fatter than ever, Elsie thought; but she kissed them both, and said she was really glad to see a Carr in her house at last. "How's your pa, Elsie — and Katy? Not laid up again, I hope."

"Oh, no; she seems to get better all the time."

"That's right," responded Mrs Worrett, heartily.

The spare room was just under the roof. It was very hot, and smelled as if the windows had never been opened since the house was built. As soon as they were alone, Elsie ran across the room, and threw up the sash; but the moment she let go, down it fell again, with a crash that shook the floor and made the pitcher dance and rattle in the washbowl. The children were dreadfully frightened especially when they heard Mrs Worrett at the foot of the stairs calling to ask what was the matter.

"It's only the window," explained Elsie, going into the hall. "I'm so sorry; but it won't stay open. Something's the matter with it."

"Did you stick the nail in?" inquired Mrs Worrett.

"The nail? No, ma'am."

"Why, how on earth did you expect it to stay up, then? You young folks never see what's before your eyes. Look on the windowsill, and you'll find it. It's put there for a purpose."

Elsie returned, much discomfited. She looked and, sure enough, there was a big nail, and there was a hole in the side of the window-frame in which to stick it. This time she got the window open without accident; but a long blue paper blind caused her much embarrassment. It hung down, and kept the air from coming in. She saw no way of fastening it.

"Roll it up and put in a pin," suggested John.

So she stuck in a couple of pins and fastened the blind out of the way. After that they looked about the room. It was plainly furnished, but very nice and neat.

"What a high bed!" Johnnie exclaimed. "Elsie, you'll have to climb on a chair to get into it; and so shall I."

Elsie felt it. "Feathers!" she cried, in a tone of horror. "Oh John! Why did we come? What shall we do?"

"I guess we shan't mind it much," replied John, who was perfectly well, and considered these little variations on home habits rather as fun than otherwise. But Elsie gave a groan. Two nights on a feather bed! How should she bear it?

Tea was ready in the kitchen when they went downstairs. A little fire had been lighted to boil the water. It was almost out, but the room felt stiflingly warm, and the butter was so nearly melted that Mrs Worrett had to help it with a teaspoon. Buzzing flies hovered above the table and gathered thick on the plate of cake. The bread was excellent, and so were the cottage cheeses and the stewed quince; but Elsie could eat nothing. She was in a fever of heat. Mrs Worrett was distressed at this want of appetite, and so was Mr Worrett, to whom the children had just been introduced.

"I'm afraid the little girl doesn't like her supper, Lucinda," he said. "You must see about getting her something different tomorrow."

"Oh! It isn't that. Everything is very nice, only I'm not hungry," pleaded Elsie, feeling as if she should like to cry.

The night was very uncomfortable. Not a breath of wind was stirring, or none found its way to the stifling bed where the little sisters lay. John slept pretty well, in spite of heat and mosquitoes, but Elsie hardly closed her eyes. Once she got up and went to the window, but the blue paper blind had become unfastened, and rattled down upon her head with a sudden bump, which startled her very much. She could find no pins in the dark, so she left it hanging, whereupon it rustled and flapped through the rest of

the night, and did its share toward keeping her
awake. About three o'clock she fell into a doze, and
it seemed only a minute after that before she woke
up to find bright sunshine in the room, and half a
dozen roosters crowing and calling under the windows. Her head ached violently. She longed to stay
in bed, but feared Mrs Worrett would think it impolite; so she dressed and went down with Johnnie, but
she looked so pale, and ate so little breakfast, that
Mrs Worrett was quite troubled and said she had
better not try to go out, but just lie on the sofa in the
best room, and amuse herself with a book.

Meanwhile Johnnie was kept in occupation by
Mrs Worrett, who had got the idea firmly fixed in her
mind that the chief joy in a child's life was to chase
chickens. Whenever a hen fluttered past the kitchen
door, which was about once in three minutes, she

would cry, "Here, Johnnie, here's another chicken for you to chase," and poor Johnnie would feel obliged to dash out into the sun. Being a very polite little girl, she did not like to say to Mrs Worrett that running in the heat was disagreeable; so by dinner-time she was thoroughly tired out, and would have been cross if she had known how; but she didn't — Johnnie was never cross. After dinner it was even worse, for the sun was hotter, and the chickens, who didn't mind sun, seemed to be walking all the time.

"Hurry, Johnnie, here's another," came so constantly, that at last Elsie grew desperate, got up, and went to the kitchen with a languid appeal, "Please, Mrs Worrett, won't you let Johnnie stay by me, because my head aches so hard?" After that, Johnnie had rest; for Mrs Worrett was the kindest of women, and had no idea that she was not amusing her little guest in the most delightful manner.

A little before six, Elsie's head felt better; and she and Johnnie put on their hats, and went for a walk in the garden. There was not much to see: beds of vegetables, a few currant bushes, that was all. Elsie was leaning against a paling, and trying to make out why the Worrett house had that queer tip-toe expression, when a sudden loud grunt startled her, and something touched the top of her head. She turned, and there was an enormous pig standing on his hind legs, on the other side of the paling. He was taller than Elsie as he stood thus, and it was his cold nose which had touched her head. Somehow, appearing

in this unexpected way, he seemed to the children like some dreadful wild beast. They screamed with fright, and fled to the house, from which Elsie never ventured to stir again during their visit. John chased chickens at intervals, but it was a doubtful pleasure and all the time she kept a wary eye on the distant pig.

When the morning came, Elsie's one thought was, would Alexander come for them in the afternoon? All day she watched the clock and the road with feverish anxiety.

About five, her anxious watch was rewarded by the appearance of a cloud of dust, out of which presently emerged old Whitey's ears and the top of the well-known carriage. They stopped at the gate. There was Alexander, brisk and smiling, very glad to see his "little misses" again, and to find them so glad to go home. Mrs Worrett, however, did not discover that they were glad; no, indeed! Elsie and John were much too polite for that. They thanked the old lady, and said goodbye so prettily that, after they were gone, she told Mr Worrett that it hadn't been a bit of trouble having them there, and she hoped they would come again, they enjoyed everything so much; only it was a pity that Elsie looked so peaked. And at that very moment Elsie was sitting on the floor of the vehicle with her head in John's lap, crying and sobbing for joy that the visit was over, and that she was on the way home.

Ah, how charming home did look, with the family

grouped in the shady porch, Katy in her white wrapper, Clover with rose-buds in her belt, and everybody ready to welcome and pet the little absentees! It was not till they were all seated round the tea-table that anybody demanded an account of the visit. Papa put the dreaded question.

"Well, Elsie, so you decided to come, after all. How was it? Why didn't you stay your week out? You look pale, it seems to me. Have you been enjoying yourself too much? Tell us all about it."

Elsie looked at Papa, and Papa looked at Elsie. Dr Carr's eyes twinkled just a little, but otherwise he was perfectly grave. Elsie began to speak, then to laugh, then to cry, and the explanation, when it came, was given in a mingled burst of all three.

"Oh, Papa, it was horrid! That is, Mrs Worrett was just as kind as could be, but so fat; and oh, such a pig! I never imagined such a pig. And that horrid sofa was so slippery that I rolled off five times, and once I hurt myself very badly. And we had a feather-bed; and I was so home-sick and I cried all the evening."

"That must have been gratifying to Mrs Worrett," put in Dr Carr.

"Oh! she didn't know it, Papa. She was asleep, and snoring so that nobody could hear. And the flies — such flies, Katy! — and the mosquitoes, and our window wouldn't open till I put in a nail. I am so glad to get home! I never want to go into the country again, never, never! Oh, if Alexander hadn't come! Why, Clover, what are you laughing for? And Dorry,

I think it's very unkind!" And Elsie ran to Katy, hid her face, and began to cry.

"Never mind, darling, they didn't mean to be unkind. Papa, her hands are quite hot; you must give her something." Katy's voice shook a little; but she would not hurt Elsie's feelings by showing that she was amused. Papa gave Elsie "something" before she went to bed — a very mild dose, I fancy; for doctors' little girls, as a general rule, don't take medicine, and next day she was much better. As the adventures of the Conic Section visit leaked out bit by bit, the family laughed till it seemed as if they would never stop. Phil was forever enacting the pig, standing on his triumphant hind legs, and patting Elsie's head with his nose; and many and many a time, "It will end like your visit to Mrs Worrett," proved a useful check when Elsie was in a self-willed mood and bent on some scheme which for the moment struck her as delightful.

A New Year and a New Plan

All at once, it seemed, it was winter, and the days flew past. Just after New Year, Doctor Carr came in and said, "Mr and Mrs Page are coming to stay with us. You once saw them, Katy, when you were about four years old and Elsie was a baby. Mrs Page was your mother's second cousin, and it is a good many years since I have seen her. Cousin Olivia writes that she is anxious to see all you children."

The Pages were arriving on Friday evening, and everyone was in a great rush beforehand making everything ready for them.

Mr Page was a tall gentleman, and Mrs Page gave the impression of being tall, although she was not. She made the children, even Katy, feel awkward and ill-at-ease, because they sensed that she was watching them and passing judgement on their ways. Behind every compliment Cousin Olivia made, Katy especially could sense her disapproval of the way things were done.

In fact, Mrs Page thought Katy too old and serious for her age, and considered her too young to take on the responsibilities of housekeeping for her father.

She also attacked Doctor Carr on the subject, and he was disturbed when he thought about it. Katy was growing old before she was twenty — he wanted her to enjoy her youth while she still had it.

After the Pages' visit, several letters came from Mrs Page and although none of the children ever knew what was in them, the outcome of them was that Doctor Carr decided to send Katy and Clover away to a boarding school called 'The Nunnery', at Hillsover on the Connecticut river. Lilly Page, Cousin Olivia's daughter, had been going there for two years already.

Neither Katy nor Clover wished to go, but no matter how much they begged, Papa's mind was made up. Even Cousin Helen approved of the idea, though wishing that the school were nearer. So the trunks were packed, everything made ready, and the last kisses given.

Papa would travel with them, but he gave them each a present before they left Burnet; Katy's present was their mother's watch, while Clover got their grandmother's watch.

Then finally they were off and, waving goodbye to the children, Katy and Clover felt that the new life opened well, and promised to be very interesting indeed.

The journey from Burnet to Hillsover took the greater part of three days, and they travelled without stopping.

Early on the third morning the train pulled into Springfield, where they were to join up with Lilly Page, whose father had brought her this far. Lilly was pretty, with delicate, rather sharp features, and her mother's stylish ease of manner. Her clothes were simple but beautifully made, and the two Carrs suddenly felt rustic and countrified.

Lilly, however, had a healthy appetite, especially for waffles, and afterwards, when it was time for her to say goodbye to her father, she began to sob and cry and cling to him hysterically.

Katy and Clover were very much embarrassed by this, knowing that Papa much preferred them to behave properly, but Lilly soon calmed down as the train set off again. On the way, she told them about the school; about the Principal, Mrs Florence, her niece, Miss Jane, the three rows of rooms — Shaker

Row, Quaker Row and Attic Row — and the view over President Searles's house where the girls could glimpse the President's youngest son Berry.

There were thirty-two rules to be kept, and to Katy's horror there was a wash-room at the end of Quaker Row where the girls had to wash on every day except Saturday. Then, they went to the Bath-house. Katy, who had been accustomed to sponge-baths every morning, was aghast, and resolved to ask Papa to do something about this.

Finally, Rose Red's name came up. Her real name was Rosamond Redding, and according to Lilly she was, "the greatest witch in the school — not exactly pretty, but sort of killing and fascinating". She was always getting into the most awful scrapes, but it seemed that she was in no danger of expulsion, as Mrs Florence was only too pleased to have Congressman Redding's daughter at her school.

It was almost evening when they reached the final stopping-place, and Lilly rushed off the train. She was wildly embracing girls who did not seem nearly as enthusiastic about her as she was about them, and had not introduced Katy and Clover to anyone. One of these girls was Rose Red herself, to whom Clover felt an instantly friendly attraction, while Rose Red too wanted to become friendly with the Carrs.

It was evident that The Nunnery was to be quite different from their expectations; but it would not be dull. Rose Red alone, with no one to help her, would be enough to prevent that.

Two ladies received them. One, a tall dignified person, was Mrs Florence; the other, with a round face, pinched lips and half-shut grey eyes, was Mrs Nipson, Mrs Florence's assistant. The two girls would be on Quaker Row, and Mrs Florence showed them their room. Doctor Carr mentioned to Mrs Florence that he would be buying a wash-stand for his daughters' room, and although Mrs Florence could not object, she did not look pleased.

After lunch, Doctor Carr left for Burnet, and although the girls did not cry, they put as much feeling into their last kisses as would have been in a dozen fits of tears.

They were not allowed to stay miserable for very long, however. Rose Red was in the room next to their own, and she and her room-mate, Mary Silver, a shy little thing who obviously adored Rose Red, were soon very good friends with Katy and Clover.

At tea time they went downstairs to the dining room. Mrs Nipson sat at the tea-tray, Mrs Florence beside her, and at the other end of the long table sat a severe-looking person that Lilly told them was "That horrid Miss Jane".

The meal was very simple and was eaten in silence, and the evening passed in deciding classes and arranging study hours.

Katy was glad when bedtime came. Among the printed rules which hung on the bedroom door, they found one which forbade talking between room-mates after the retiring-bell had been rung.

But after the candle was blown out, Clover whispered very softly, "Do you think you're going to like it?"

"I'm not quite sure," answered Katy in the same cautious whisper.

And so ended the first day at The Nunnery.

Roses and Thorns

The rising-bell rang at six o'clock, startling Katy and Clover. After breakfast, lessons began, and went on until one o'clock. Dinner followed, with an hour's "recreation", then the bell rang for "silent study hour", when the girls sat with their books in their rooms but were not allowed to speak to each other. Next came a walk.

Katy and Clover enjoyed the walk. Lilly, just in front of them, amused them with stories of the different girls she pointed out. Esther Dearborn, Rose Red's friend — handsome, but terribly sarcastic; Amy Alsop and Ellen Grey — nice enough, but so distressingly good. Why did Katy want to know about the nasty little pigtailed Bella Arkwright? That girl with pink velvet on her hat was Louisa Agnew, whose family were not at all in society — Lilly believed her father painted portraits.

Next day was Saturday, but there was a lot to be done. Early in the morning it was their turn to go to the bath-house, and Rose got into trouble by fastening her towel, sponge and soap to her hat.

Before six weeks were over, Katy and Clover felt as if they had lived at Hillsover for years, and although they both loved Rose Red, her pranks sometimes got them into trouble. Rose felt dreadful about these occasions, and always pleaded and begged, but Mrs Florence was not to be moved. She had secretly decided to leave the school at Midsummer, and now took no pains to study character, or give out justice carefully.

As they settled down into their new life Katy was very much shocked and displeased by the behaviour of the girls towards the young men in the college next door.

"I declare I've a good mind to get up a society to put down flirting," she said one day.

"Do," said Rose. "What fun it would be! Call it 'The Society for the Suppression of Young Men'. I'll join."

Katy was slightly taken aback by the idea of Rose being totally in favour of her idea, but in the end she agreed that she would form a society, and they called it 'The Society for the Suppression of Unlady-like Conduct'.

"Only we'll say 'The S.S.U.C.'," said Rose. "That sounds brisk and snappy and will drive the whole school wild with curiosity. What larks! How I long to begin!"

The S.S.U.C. first met on the next Saturday afternoon. Katy was elected President, and Rose was Secretary, and a list of laws and bye-laws was drawn up. Some members read out amusing poems they had written, and then the newly formed society played a game, resulting in much lady-like mirth.

"Well," demanded Lilly later, "so how did the high and mighty meeting go off?" She had refused to join the S.S.U.C.

"*Delicious!*" replied Rose, smacking her lips. "But you mustn't ask questions, Lilly. Our proceedings are strictly private."

"I think you're mean!" cried Lilly. Then she said to herself, "They're just trying to tease. I know it was stupid."

Injustice

One Saturday morning in June, Katy and Clover returned from the bath-house to find their possessions being bundled out of their bright sunny room to a much smaller, darker room at the end of Quaker Row that nobody had wanted to take. Both were completely bewildered.

What had happened? Why were they being moved? Miss Jane treated them both as if they had done something wrong, and Katy, feeling her temper rise, marched straight to Mrs Florence's office, demanding to know what had happened.

A note had been found in Berry Searles's pocket, signed "Miss Carr" and asking the young man to send the writer some cake. Neither Katy nor Clover had ever seen the note before, and the handwriting was very different from their own, but no member of the staff was prepared to listen to them or discuss it further. They were even told that they were fortunate not to be expelled from the school.

Katy was extremely angry at this total lack of justice, and told Mrs Florence that she would instantly write to her father, so that he would remove herself and Clover from such a school.

The two Carrs and their friends were heartbroken to think that they could be so treated, but that night Katy reconsidered her decision. If they left, she and Clover would straight away be thought guilty of writing that note, and Papa, who had wanted them to go to school for a year, would be very upset and disappointed.

So Katy informed Mrs Florence of her decision to stay, in such an honest and sincere manner that Mrs Florence felt rather disturbed by what had taken place, although she would not reconsider.

Soon after this, Rose Red rushed to find Katy and Clover, and tell them a secret she had just discovered.

"You promise not to tell?" she asked, and then stopped and sniffed the air. "That wretched little Bella Arkwright is hiding in here. I can smell that horrid pomatum she puts on her hair."

A brief search ensued. The child was found, and roundly scolded by Rose Red before being ejected from the room.

"Well, then," she said, resuming her story, "Mrs Florence is going away the week after next, and what's more — she's going to be married!"

It was true! Rose Red had overheard a conversation between two members of staff, and had also received a letter from her sister Sylvia, who knew this to be a fact. A present now had to be bought and presented to Mrs Florence. After much discussion, Sylvia Redding was chosen to buy the present, and Katy elected to present it, although she was reluctant to do so after the affair of the note.

The gift was a delicate basket of silver wire, and the girls filled it with roses from a nearby garden. Then Katy presented it to Mrs Florence.

Mrs Florence was surprised and very touched. "Tell the girls I thank them very much," she said, with tears in her eyes. "Their present is beautiful. I shall always value it!"

When Mrs Florence left the following week, the school was left in Mrs Nipson's care, and she soon put her ideas about food into practice. Thick slices of batter pudding with a few blackberries on top took the place of meat three times a week in the warm weather, and although they were thick slices, the girls still felt hungry after eating them. When National Independence Day, July the Fourth, came round, most girls — especially Rose Red — made themselves sick on all the sweets and cakes they ordered in celebration.

Summer was hot and drowsy that year, and after the college next door closed for vacation, everything seemed very dull and quiet. Both teachers and scholars were glad when the middle of September arrived, and with it the opening of the autumn vacation.

The Autumn Vacation

Katy and Clover were not returning to Burnet that vacation, but were spending it instead with Lilly's family. So Katy was not half as happy as the other girls, although she and Clover felt as excited as the rest waving goodbye to Mrs Nipson.

At six o'clock the train reached Springfield, where Mr Page was waiting for Lilly and her cousins. He greeted them so kindly that their forlorn feeling at not going home fled at once, and he took his three charges to the large hotel, where rooms were already booked.

"Now for waffles," whispered Lilly excitedly. The two waiters flew to her side and provided her with waffle after waffle until even *her* appetite became jaded.

Next morning, Louisa Agnew met them at the station. She had spent the night with an uncle, and was now to be in Mr Page's care until they reached Ashburn. Lilly's attitude to her was so cold and even impolite that she earned a rebuke from her father, who admired Mr Agnew, the painter.

The size and splendour of the Pages' house dazzled the two Carrs. There were marble floors, busts and statues everywhere, and Mrs Page always looked as though she were dressed for a party.

Katy and Clover changed for dinner, but Mrs Page was not impressed by their clothes, and had already engaged a dressmaker for them. Katy was reluctant to allow this, but the entrance of Lilly's brother Clarence put an end to the discussion. He was a square, freckled boy of thirteen, with reddish hair, who did not offer to shake hands with his cousins, but said, "How d'you do?" in a sulky voice, and buried his nose in a glass of milk.

His mother seemed unable to let him alone, with her constant correcting of his manners, although these were certainly bad. But he was a droll little chap, and bright too, and would be very pleasant if he was not picked on so much.

Mrs Page stuck to her promise of buying clothes, and soon the Carrs both had new dresses, everything fitting perfectly and having that air of finish which they had noticed and admired in Lilly's clothes.

A little later, Clover made friends with Clarence, and discovered him to be pleasant and good-tempered when he was left alone. Tactfully Clover rebuked him for his argumentativeness with Lilly, and far from being offended, Clarence grew very

fond of his cousin Clover, and heeded her more than anyone else.

A few days before the vacation ended, Katy and Clover went to spend a day with Louisa and her family. The Agnews lived in a far less fashionable street than the Pages, but the Carrs instantly felt more comfortable and at home there. The house was full of drawings and paintings done by Mr Agnew, which made a lovely and unusual change from the marble of the Page house, and Katy and Clover agreed that dinner at the Agnews was the merriest they had had since leaving home.

A few days later they left for Hillsover. Clarence's friendship, and the remembrance of their day with the Agnews were the pleasantest things that the girls carried away with them from their autumn vacation.

Christmas Boxes

October was a delightful month, but early in November it became very cold. Katy and Clover's room was chilly, a foretaste of what winter was to be.

Towards the end of November Miss Jane caught a heavy cold, and was forced to go to bed, where she stayed for four weeks. Everyone felt great relief at her absence, even Katy, until one night she heard Miss Jane coughing violently. The next day she went in to see the teacher, and contentedly cleaned and tidied the room for Miss Jane, quickly and quietly. Rose Red and Clover were incredulous.

"My stars!" exclaimed Rose. "You didn't really? And she hasn't bitten your head off?"

Katy laughed. "Not a bit. And what's more, I'm going again."

She was as good as her word. During a conversation with Miss Jane, the teacher discovered that Katy had been ill and confined to bed herself for four years, and after that, Katy fancied that she looked at her in a new and kinder way.

Christmas fell on a Friday that year, and it was very cold indeed. On the Thursday evening, the sledge brought two boxes, both for Katy and Clover. Mrs Nipson had the nails taken out and the boxes taken to their room, but the girls could not look at what was inside until the morning.

That night, Katy and Clover went to sleep as quickly as possible, and Katy dreamed of home, waking up with excitement before dawn.

After breakfast they opened the large box, Rose innocently coming in as they began, as if by accident. Inside it there were four boxes full of different cakes, round which all sorts of parcels and bundles had been tightly packed — two knitted hoods from Elsie, books from Dorry, inkstands and pen-handles from Phil and Johnnie, and two beautiful gold watch chains from papa. Cecy had sent ribbons; there were tape-measures, thread-cases and a bag full of hickory nuts from the servants, and beneath all this were figs, prunes, almonds, raisins, candy, apples and pears. There seemed no end to the surprises. When at last everything was out, the girls divided all the sweets and cakes into little parcels for the girls, whose own Christmas boxes had been snowed up and did not arrive until Monday.

After dinner, the smaller box was opened, and proved to contain flowers and two quilted silk glove-cases from Cousin Helen. Katy then took some of the flowers and some fruit along to Miss Jane, and wished her a merry Christmas.

Later, Miss Jane called her, and rather hastily said, "Miss Carr, I made up my mind some time since that we did you an injustice last term. It is your general conduct, and the good influence which I have seen you exert over the other girls, which convinced me that we must have been wrong about you. I shall say the same to Mrs Nipson."

Katy nearly kissed her, but instead she shook hands heartily, and ran to tell Clover. And of all that she had received, Katy considered that conversation with Miss Jane as her very best Christmas box.

School was a much happier place after this, although the long winter was very cold indeed, Clover especially feeling it.

To keep themselves occupied during the cold months, the girls resorted to all sorts of devices — tatting, embroidery, lace-making, and autograph-collecting were just some of them.

During this time, little Bella Arkwright's father died, and it was too far for her to go home. Katy liked children, and seeing the child's grief, was especially kind to her, which Bella repaid with the gift of her whole heart, while looking at Katy with a curious expression, as if she had something on her mind.

At last February arrived, and with it St Valentine's Day.

Katy and Clover received a card each from Phil, while Miss Jane had one supposed to come from a cannibal who had just eaten her fiancé, the missionary Mr Hardhack. Miss Jane was furious, but no one ever found out who the culprit was: it was in fact Rose Red, whose revenge it was on Miss Jane for her unjust treatment of Katy and Clover before.

And now it was only six weeks to the end of term.

Although Katy's heart bounded with gladness at the thought of home, she was slightly sorry to leave, and said to Clover, "Home is lovely, and I would rather be there than anywhere else; but if you and I live to be a hundred, we shall never be girls at a boarding-school again."

With only seven days to go, the girls received a letter from Papa saying that he would not be able to come to the school to fetch them. This was a great disappointment, especially when given the thought that they would have to travel with strangers, friends of Mrs Hall's, that Papa had spoken to.

On the last evening, Bella followed Katy to her room and, weeping and sobbing, admitted that she had written the note for which Katy and Clover had

been punished. Katy was almost too surprised for words, but managed to comfort the poor child and kiss her in forgiveness.

Rose was not returning to school either, and there were many tears at their parting. But promises were made of visits to be paid and letters to be sent and received, and as Katy and Clover drove away the girls waved from their windows in farewell.

The journey was smooth but very slow indeed, as they were returning by boat. At last, in the afternoon of the third day, Burnet was in sight.

Standing on the edge of the dock was Papa, who was not released for some time once his two daughters reached his arms. As they reached the house, the children came pouring out to greet them, and Cecy came over to hug them as she had done when she was twelve, even though they were all older now.

The Blue-room had been transformed into Katy and Clover's new room, and everything in it was very pretty, while the supper they all had that night was very gay. Elsie poured the tea, while Clover and Katy sat on either side of Papa — Katy would begin her old duties tomorrow.

And with that morrow, when she came out of her pretty room and took her place once more as manager of the household, her grown-up life may be said to have begun.